B. C. On The Rocks

by Johnny Hart

A FAWCETT GOLD MEDAL BOOK

Fawcett Publications, Inc., Greenwich, Conn.

Fawcett Gold Medal Books by Johnny Hart:

50¢ Wherever Paperbacks Are Sold

If your bookdealer is sold out, send cover price plus 15¢ for postage and handling to Mail Order Service, Fawcett Publications, Inc., Greenwich, Conn. Please order by number and title. No Canadian orders.

B.C. ON THE ROCKS

Copyright © 1966, 1967 by Publishers News Syndicate, Inc.

Copyright © 1971 by Fawcett Publications, Inc.

Printed in the United States of America.

December 1971

SLUUP

I NEGLECTED TO CONSIDER THE LAW OF SUCTION.

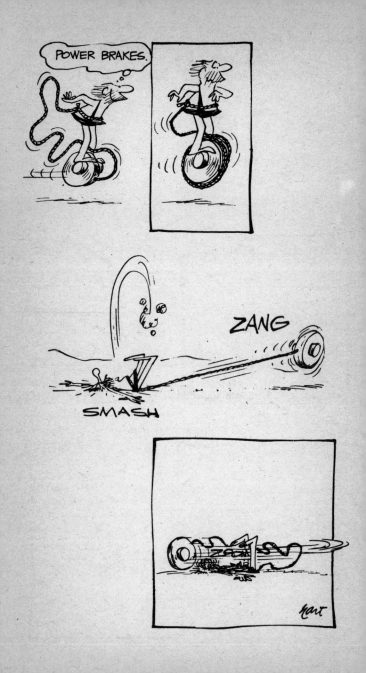

HOW 'BOUT A PIGGY-BACK RIDE?

HOW BOUT THAT.

ZIP

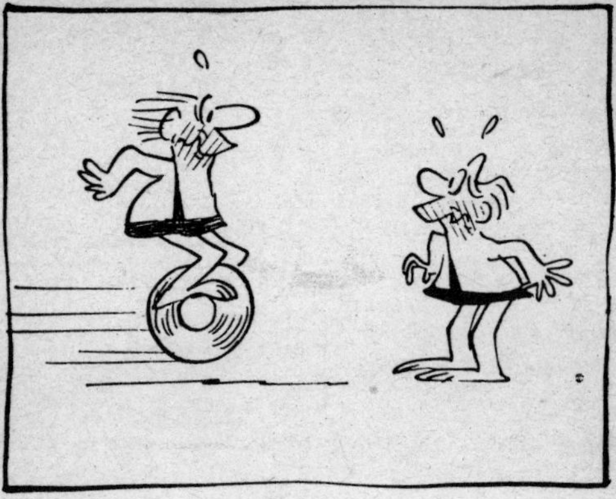

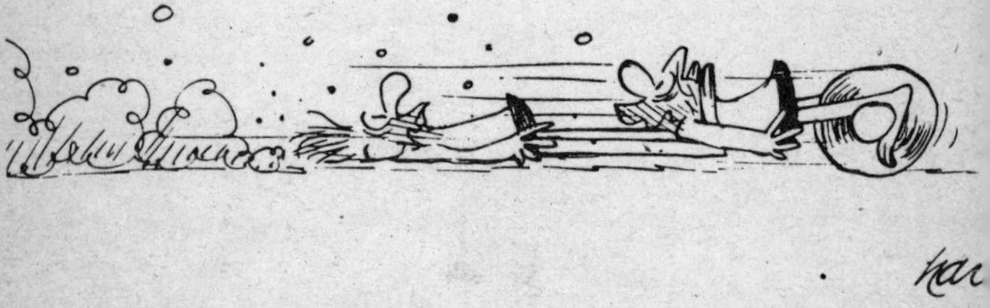

law *n.* a rule, which when disobeyed,

sets us apart from others.

SEE hoosegow.

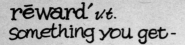

rēward′ *v.t.*
something you get –

for doing something
you wouldn't ordinarily do –

if it wasn't for the reward.

friend'ship *n.* that which occurs when each of two parties—

sense prominence through the other's stupidity.

lăn'guage *n.* a combination of sounds emitted through an orifice in the front of the skull.

often to the discomfort-

of the two aperatures on the sides of the skull.

hart

nothing n.

hart

tree. *n.* any of a
number of giant
fruit bearing –

and/or leafy plants.

(RARE. *found in housing
developments.*)

rock (RŎK) n.

to cause something
or someone to sway-

by hitting them with it.

hart

lēad'er *n.* a person who makes an important decision,

then sits back,

and answers stupid questions for the rest of his life.

hip *n.* that broad part of the body—

on which the hands rest in anger.

especially on women.

nŏn'sense ✻ *n.*

bōne *n.* one of a group of moving parts—

which moved too slowly—

to avoid being buried by a dog.

hart

in which mudballs are trump.

ĂNNŌY, ..TO SNORE, TO TALK, TO BURP, TO STARE, TO YELL, TO WALK, ...

YOU HAVE A DUPLICATION HERE.

HOW'S THAT?

YOU COVERED ALL THIS UNDER 'EXĬST'

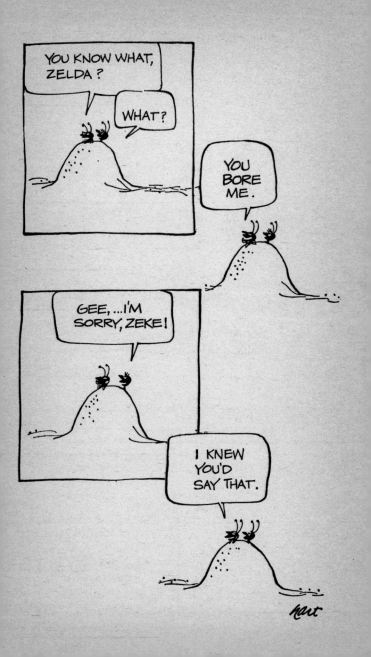

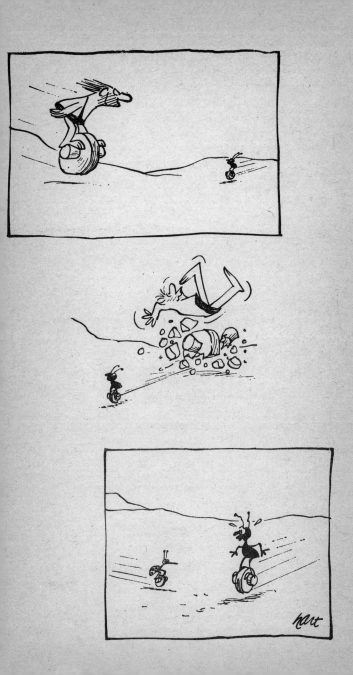